W9-AHP-314

Student Edition

BUILD
BELOW THE BASELINE

*Developing the Part of Your
Life that Only God Sees*

PAUL CHAPPELL

Copyright © 2016 by Striving Together Publications. All Scripture quotations are taken from the King James Version.

First published in 2016 by Striving Together Publications, a ministry of Lancaster Baptist Church, Lancaster, CA 93535. Striving Together Publications is committed to providing tried, trusted, and proven books that will further equip local churches to carry out the Great Commission. Your comments and suggestions are valued.

All rights reserved. No part of this book may be reproduced, stored in a retrieval system, or transmitted in any form or by any means—electronic, mechanical, photocopy, recording, or otherwise—without written permission of the publisher, except for brief quotations in printed reviews.

Striving Together Publications
4020 E. Lancaster Blvd.
Lancaster, CA 93535
800.201.7748

Cover design by Andrew Jones
Layout by Craig Parker
Edited by Joy Lemke

The author and publication team have put forth every effort to give proper credit to quotes and thoughts that are not original with the author. It is not our intent to claim originality with any quote or thought that could not readily be tied to an original source.

ISBN 978-1-59894-331-3
Printed in the United States of America

Contents

1. A Relationship with God 5

2. Trust in God 13

3. Repentance. 25

4. Humility 39

5. A Good Conscience 49

6. Dying to Self 61

7. Filled with the Spirit. 73

8. Spiritual Discipline 83

9. Forgiveness. 93

10. Contentment 101

A Relationship with God

Text

PHILIPPIANS 3:10–14

10 *That I may know him, and the power of his resurrection, and the fellowship of his sufferings, being made conformable unto his death;*

11 *If by any means I might attain unto the resurrection of the dead.*

12 *Not as though I had already attained, either were already perfect: but I follow after, if that I may apprehend that for which also I am apprehended of Christ Jesus.*

13 *Brethren, I count not myself to have apprehended: but this one thing I do, forgetting those things which are behind, and reaching forth unto those things which are before,*

14 *I press toward the mark for the prize of the high calling of God in Christ Jesus.*

Overview

The greatest privilege of life is knowing Christ. There are many benefits of the Christian life, and they are discovered through the course of a lifetime. In this study, we will look at the parts of the Christian life that no one else sees—the elements that comprise our foundation.

It may be easy for a while to portray an image of spiritual success when there is no real substance underneath. We may even have those closest to us fooled into thinking that everything is fine. In fact, one may be fooling himself into thinking that everything is okay because the outward structure looks right. But long before the destruction of a life is seen on the outside, there are issues with the foundation developing below the surface. Every structurally-sound life has a common denominator—it is built on a solid foundation.

Introduction

_____

_____

_____

PHILIPPIANS 3:9
9   *And be found in him, not having mine own righteousness, which is of the law, but that which is through the faith of Christ, the righteousness which is of God by faith.*

JOHN 15:5
5   *I am the vine, ye are the branches…*

EPHESIANS 2:19–22
19 *Now therefore ye are no more strangers and foreigners, but fellowcitizens with the saints, and of the household of God;*
20 *And are built upon the foundation of the apostles and prophets, Jesus Christ himself being the chief corner stone;*
21 *In whom all the building fitly framed together groweth unto an holy temple in the Lord:*
22 *In whom ye also are builded together for an habitation of God through the Spirit.*

I. The Foundation of _Relationships_

PHILIPPIANS 3:10

10 That I may know him, and the power of his resurrection, and the fellowship of his sufferings, being made conformable unto his death;

A. Know His _Person_

EPHESIANS 1:15–18

15 Wherefore I also, after I heard of your faith in the Lord Jesus, and love unto all the saints,

16 Cease not to give thanks for you, making mention of you in my prayers;

17 That the God of our Lord Jesus Christ, the Father of glory, may give unto you the spirit of wisdom and revelation in the knowledge of him:

18 The eyes of your understanding being enlightened; that ye may know what is the hope of his calling, and what the riches of the glory of his inheritance in the saints,

B. Know His _Power_

2 PETER 1:3

3 According as his divine power hath given unto us all things that pertain unto life and godliness, through the knowledge of him that hath called us to glory and virtue:

1 CORINTHIANS 2:1–5

1 And I, brethren, when I came to you, came not with excellency of speech or of wisdom, declaring unto you the testimony of God.

2   For I determined not to know any thing among you, save Jesus Christ, and him crucified.

3   And I was with you in weakness, and in fear, and in much trembling.

4   And my speech and my preaching was not with enticing words of man's wisdom, **but in demonstration of the Spirit and of power:**

5   That your faith should not stand in the wisdom of men, but **in the power of God.**

C. Know His _Presence_

HEBREWS 4:15-16

15   For we have not a high priest which cannot be touched with the feeling of our infirmities; but was in all points tempted like as we are, yet without sin.

16   Let us therefore come boldly unto the throne of grace, that we may obtain mercy, and find grace to help in time of need.

II. The Formation of _Faith_

PHILIPPIANS 3:11-12

11   If by any means I might attain unto the resurrection of the dead.

12   Not as though I had already attained, either were already perfect: but I follow after, if that I may apprehend that for which also I am apprehended of Christ Jesus.

A. The Promise of _Resurrection_

EPHESIANS 2:1, 5–6

1 And you hath he quickened, who were dead in trespasses and sins;

5 Even when we were dead in sins, hath quickened us together with Christ, (by grace ye are saved;)

6 And hath raised us up together, and made us sit together in heavenly places in Christ Jesus:

GALATIANS 2:20

20 I am crucified with Christ: nevertheless I live; yet not I, but Christ liveth in me: and the life which I now live in the flesh I live by the faith of the Son of God, who loved me, and gave himself for me.

ROMANS 6:11

11 Likewise reckon ye also yourselves to be dead indeed unto sin, but alive unto God through Jesus Christ our Lord.

COLOSSIANS 3:1

1 If ye then be risen with Christ, seek those things which are above, where Christ sitteth on the right hand of God.

B. The Process of _Transformation_

ROMANS 8:29

29 For whom he did foreknow, he also did predestinate to be conformed to the image of his Son, that he might be the firstborn among many brethren.

III. The Fixation of _Will_

PHILIPPIANS 3:13–14

13   Brethren, I count not myself to have apprehended: but this one thing I do, forgetting those things which are behind, and reaching forth unto those things which are before,

14   I press toward the mark for the prize of the high calling of God in Christ Jesus.

A. Paul Recognized His _Position_

B. Paul Rejected the _Past_

C. Paul Ran to Win the _Prize_

HEBREWS 12:2

2   Looking unto Jesus the author and finisher of our faith; who for the joy that was set before him endured the cross, despising the shame, and is set down at the right hand of the throne of God.

Conclusion

2 TIMOTHY 4:6–7

6   For I am now ready to be offered, and the time of my departure is at hand.

7   I have fought a good fight, I have finished my course, I have kept the faith:

_____

_____

_____

Study Questions

1. What is the greatest privilege of life?

   Knowing Christ sal

2. What three ways to know Christ did Paul give us in Philippians 3:10?

3. What does Romans 8:29 tell us is God's ultimate goal for our transformation?

4. What are two or three ways you can purposefully grow in your relationship with the Lord?

5. God intends that we grow in our relationship with Him and, as a byproduct, in our Christian maturity. What is one way you see the Lord growing you as a Christian right now?

6. What has changed (transformed) in your life since the time you were saved?

7. At the conclusion of Paul's race, he could say that he had been faithful to the end. Have you made a deliberate decision to finish strong? If not, do so now and record the date below.

Memory Verse

PHILIPPIANS 3:10

10 *That I may know him, and the power of his resurrection, and the fellowship of his sufferings, being made conformable unto his death;*

Trust in God

Text

1 KINGS 17:1–16

1   And Elijah the Tishbite, who was of the inhabitants of Gilead, said unto Ahab, As the LORD God of Israel liveth, before whom I stand, there shall not be dew nor rain these years, but according to my word.

2   And the word of the LORD came unto him, saying,

3   Get thee hence, and turn thee eastward, and hide thyself by the brook Cherith, that is before Jordan.

4   And it shall be, that thou shalt drink of the brook; and I have commanded the ravens to feed thee there.

5   So he went and did according unto the word of the LORD: for he went and dwelt by the brook Cherith, that is before Jordan.

6   And the ravens brought him bread and flesh in the morning, and bread and flesh in the evening; and he drank of the brook.

7   And it came to pass after a while, that the brook dried up, because there had been no rain in the land.

8   And the word of the LORD came unto him, saying,

9   Arise, get thee to Zarephath, which belongeth to Zidon, and dwell there: behold, I have commanded a widow woman there to sustain thee.

10   So he arose and went to Zarephath. And when he came to the gate of the city, behold, the widow woman was there

gathering of sticks: and he called to her, and said, Fetch me, I pray thee, a little water in a vessel, that I may drink.

11   And as she was going to fetch it, he called to her, and said, Bring me, I pray thee, a morsel of bread in thine hand.

12   And she said, As the LORD thy God liveth, I have not a cake, but an handful of meal in a barrel, and a little oil in a cruse: and, behold, I am gathering two sticks, that I may go in and dress it for me and my son, that we may eat it, and die.

13   And Elijah said unto her, Fear not; go and do as thou hast said: but make me thereof a little cake first, and bring it unto me, and after make for thee and for thy son.

14   For thus saith the LORD God of Israel, The barrel of meal shall not waste, neither shall the cruse of oil fail, until the day that the LORD sendeth rain upon the earth.

15   And she went and did according to the saying of Elijah: and she, and he, and her house, did eat many days.

16   And the barrel of meal wasted not, neither did the cruse of oil fail, according to the word of the LORD, which he spake by Elijah.

Overview

Everyone possesses trust. It is the *object* of our trust that makes the difference when it is put to the test. It is at a time of trial that the source of our trust will be revealed.

As someone once said, "A faith that cannot be tested cannot be trusted." In this study, we discover how to develop a faith that can be trusted. As we look in 1 Kings 17 at the prophet Elijah and a widow in Zarephath, we will see how their trust was tested, although in different ways. Both passed the test and experienced the incredible provision of God.

Introduction

_____

_____

_____

DEUTERONOMY 11:13–17

13 *And it shall come to pass, if ye shall hearken diligently unto my commandments which I command you this day, to love the LORD your God, and to serve him with all your heart and with all your soul,*

14 *That I will give you the rain of your land in his due season, the first rain and the latter rain, that thou mayest gather in thy corn, and thy wine, and thine oil.*

15 *And I will send grass in thy fields for thy cattle, that thou mayest eat and be full.*

16 *Take heed to yourselves, that your heart be not deceived, and ye turn aside, and serve other gods, and worship them;*

17 *And then the LORD's wrath be kindled against you, and he shut up the heaven, that there be no rain, and that the land yield not her fruit; and lest ye perish quickly from off the good land which the LORD giveth you.*

1 KINGS 17:1

1 *And Elijah the Tishbite, who was of the inhabitants of Gilead, said unto Ahab, As the LORD God of Israel liveth, before whom I stand, there shall not be dew nor rain these years, but according to my word.*

I. The _____ of Elijah

1 KINGS 17:2–5

2   And the word of the LORD came unto him, saying,

3   Get thee hence, and turn thee eastward, and hide thyself by the brook Cherith, that is before Jordan.

4   And it shall be, that thou shalt drink of the brook; and I have commanded the ravens to feed thee there.

5   So he went and did according unto the word of the LORD: for he went and dwelt by the brook Cherith, that is before Jordan.

A. To Go to _Cherith_

1 KINGS 17:3

3   …hide thyself by the brook Cherith…

1 KINGS 17:5–6

5   So he went and did according unto the word of the LORD: for he went and dwelt by the brook Cherith, that is before Jordan.

6   And the ravens brought him bread and flesh in the morning, and bread and flesh in the evening; and he drank of the brook.

PROVERBS 3:5–6

5   Trust in the LORD with all thine heart; and lean not unto thine own understanding.

6   In all thy ways acknowledge him, and he shall direct thy paths.

PSALM 18:30

30   As for God, his way is perfect: the word of the LORD is tried: he is a buckler to all those that trust in him.

ROMANS 14:23

23   And he that doubteth is damned if he eat, because he eateth not of faith: for whatsoever is not of faith is sin.

HEBREWS 11:1, 6

1   Now faith is the substance of things hoped for, the evidence of things not seen.

6   But without faith it is impossible to please him…

B. To Go to _____ *Zarephath*

1 KINGS 17:9–10

9   Arise, get thee to Zarephath, which belongeth to Zidon, and dwell there…

10   So he arose and went to Zarephath…

1 KINGS 17:9

9   …behold, I have commanded a widow woman there to sustain thee.

ISAIAH 55:8

8   For my thoughts are not your thoughts, neither are your ways my ways, saith the LORD.

JEREMIAH 29:11

11   For I know the thoughts that I think toward you, saith the LORD, thoughts of peace, and not of evil, to give you an expected end.

LUKE 12:27–31

27   Consider the lilies how they grow: they toil not, they spin not; and yet I say unto you, that Solomon in all his glory was not arrayed like one of these.

28 *If then God so clothe the grass, which is to day in the field, and to morrow is cast into the oven; how much more will he clothe you, O ye of little faith?*

29 *And seek not ye what ye shall eat, or what ye shall drink, neither be ye of doubtful mind.*

30 *For all these things do the nations of the world seek after: and your Father knoweth that ye have need of these things.*

31 *But rather seek ye the kingdom of God; and all these things shall be added unto you.*

II. The _____Test_____ of the Widow

1 KINGS 17:10–12

10 *So he arose and went to Zarephath. And when he came to the gate of the city, behold, the widow woman was there gathering of sticks: and he called to her, and said, Fetch me, I pray thee, a little water in a vessel, that I may drink.*

11 *And as she was going to fetch it, he called to her, and said, Bring me, I pray thee, a morsel of bread in thine hand.*

12 *And she said, As the LORD thy God liveth, I have not a cake, but an handful of meal in a barrel, and a little oil in a cruse: and, behold, I am gathering two sticks, that I may go in and dress it for me and my son, that we may eat it, and die.*

A. Her _Residence_

B. Her _Resources_

JOHN 6:8–13

8   One of his disciples, Andrew, Simon Peter's brother, saith unto him,

9   There is a lad here, which hath five barley loaves, and two small fishes: but what are they among so many?

10   And Jesus said, Make the men sit down. Now there was much grass in the place. So the men sat down, in number about five thousand.

11   And Jesus took the loaves; and when he had given thanks, he distributed to the disciples, and the disciples to them that were set down; and likewise of the fishes as much as they would.

12   When they were filled, he said unto his disciples, Gather up the fragments that remain, that nothing be lost.

13   Therefore they gathered them together, and filled twelve baskets with the fragments of the five barley loaves, which remained over and above unto them that had eaten.

C. Her *Reasoning*

1 KINGS 17:12

12   …behold, I am gathering two sticks, that I may go in and dress it for me and my son, that we may eat it, and die.

PROVERBS 3:5–6

5   Trust in the LORD with all thine heart; and lean not unto thine own understanding.

6   In all thy ways acknowledge him, and he shall direct thy paths.

PROVERBS 14:12

12 *There is a way which seemeth right unto a man,*
But the end thereof are the ways of death.

III. The _____Triumph_____ of Faith

1 KINGS 17:13–16

13 *And Elijah said unto her, Fear not; go and do as thou*
hast said: but make me thereof a little cake first, and bring
it unto me, and after make for thee and for thy son.
14 *For thus saith the LORD God of Israel, The barrel*
of meal shall not waste, neither shall the cruse of oil fail,
until the day that the LORD sendeth rain upon the earth.
15 *And she went and did according to the saying of*
Elijah: and she, and he, and her house, did eat many days.
16 *And the barrel of meal wasted not, neither did the*
cruse of oil fail, according to the word of the LORD, which
he spake by Elijah.

A. The _____Request_____ from the Prophet

1 KINGS 17:13

13 *And Elijah said unto her, Fear not; go and do as*
thou hast said: but make me thereof a little cake first,
and bring it unto me, and after make for thee and for
thy son.

PROVERBS 3:9–10

9 *Honour the LORD with thy substance, and with the*
firstfruits of all thine increase:

10 So shall thy barns be filled with plenty, and thy
presses shall burst out with new wine.

MALACHI 3:10
10 Bring ye all the tithes into the storehouse, that
there may be meat in mine house, **and prove me now
herewith**, saith the LORD of hosts, if I will not open you
the windows of heaven, and pour you out a blessing,
that there shall not be room enough to receive it.

B. The _Response_ **of the Widow**

1 KINGS 17:15
15 And she went and did according to the saying
of Elijah…

JOB 36:15
15 He delivereth the poor in his affliction, and
openeth their ears in oppression.

PSALM 37:25
25 I have been young, and now am old; yet have I not
seen the righteous forsaken, nor his seed begging bread.

C. The _Resource_ **Supplied**

1 KINGS 17:15–16
15 …and she, and he, and her house, did eat
many days.
16 And the barrel of meal wasted not, neither did the
cruse of oil fail, according to the word of the LORD,
which he spake by Elijah.

Luke 6:38

38 *Give, and it shall be given unto you; good measure, pressed down, and shaken together, and running over, shall men give into your bosom. For with the same measure that ye mete withal it shall be measured to you again.*

Philippians 4:19

19 *But my God shall supply all your need according to his riches in glory by Christ Jesus.*

Conclusion

_____

_____

_____

Study Questions

1. When Elijah told the Israelites that God would send a drought as judgment because they turned to other gods, from where did he receive that message?

2. In what ways did Elijah display his trust in God?

3. What does Proverbs 14:12 tell us about taking the path that makes sense by our reasoning?

4. What are some Scriptures (perhaps even in this lesson) that encourage us to trust God with our direction and provision?

5. In what ways was the widow woman's reasoning faulty? How did relying on her reasoning almost cause her to miss God's provision?

6. Has there been a time when God has directed you to do something that did not make sense to you? How did He show you His power when you trusted and obeyed?

7. In Philippians 4:19 God promises to meet our needs. What does this verse say is the source from which He meets them? Can this source ever run dry?

8. One of the best ways to encourage our faith is to remember how God has provided in the past. What are some ways in your life that God has provided for you in a time of need?

Memory Verses

PROVERBS 3:5–6

5 *Trust in the LORD with all thine heart; and lean not unto thine own understanding.*
6 *In all thy ways acknowledge him, and he shall direct thy paths.*

Repentance

Discern sins
Pride
Controlled anger
Lust
Unforgiveness

Text

1 CHRONICLES 21

1   *And Satan stood up against Israel, and provoked David to number Israel.*

2   *And David said to Joab and to the rulers of the people, Go, number Israel from Beersheba even to Dan; and bring the number of them to me, that I may know it.*

3   *And Joab answered, The LORD make his people an hundred times so many more as they be: but, my lord the king, are they not all my lord's servants? why then doth my lord require this thing? why will he be a cause of trespass to Israel?*

4   *Nevertheless the king's word prevailed against Joab. Wherefore Joab departed, and went throughout all Israel, and came to Jerusalem.*

5   *And Joab gave the sum of the number of the people unto David. And all they of Israel were a thousand thousand and an hundred thousand men that drew sword: and Judah was four hundred threescore and ten thousand men that drew sword.*

6   *But Levi and Benjamin counted he not among them: for the king's word was abominable to Joab.*

7   *And God was displeased with this thing; therefore he smote Israel.*

8   *And David said unto God, I have sinned greatly, because I have done this thing: but now, I beseech thee, do away the iniquity of thy servant; for I have done very foolishly.*

9   *And the LORD spake unto Gad, David's seer, saying,*

10 *Go and tell David, saying, Thus saith the* Lord, *I offer thee three things: choose thee one of them, that I may do it unto thee.*

11 *So Gad came to David, and said unto him, Thus saith the* Lord, *Choose thee*

12 *Either three years' famine; or three months to be destroyed before thy foes, while that the sword of thine enemies overtaketh thee; or else three days the sword of the* Lord, *even the pestilence, in the land, and the angel of the* Lord *destroying throughout all the coasts of Israel. Now therefore advise thyself what word I shall bring again to him that sent me.*

13 *And David said unto Gad, I am in a great strait: let me fall now into the hand of the* Lord; *for very great are his mercies: but let me not fall into the hand of man.*

14 *So the* Lord *sent pestilence upon Israel: and there fell of Israel seventy thousand men.*

15 *And God sent an angel unto Jerusalem to destroy it: and as he was destroying, the* Lord *beheld, and he repented him of the evil, and said to the angel that destroyed, It is enough, stay now thine hand. And the angel of the* Lord *stood by the threshingfloor of Ornan the Jebusite.*

16 *And David lifted up his eyes, and saw the angel of the* Lord *stand between the earth and the heaven, having a drawn sword in his hand stretched out over Jerusalem. Then David and the elders of Israel, who were clothed in sackcloth, fell upon their faces.*

17 *And David said unto God, Is it not I that commanded the people to be numbered? even I it is that have sinned and done evil indeed; but as for these sheep, what have they done?*

let thine hand, I pray thee, O Lord my God, be on me, and on my father's house; but not on thy people, that they should be plagued.

18 Then the angel of the Lord commanded Gad to say to David, that David should go up, and set up an altar unto the Lord in the threshingfloor of Ornan the Jebusite.

19 And David went up at the saying of Gad, which he spake in the name of the Lord.

20 And Ornan turned back, and saw the angel; and his four sons with him hid themselves. Now Ornan was threshing wheat.

21 And as David came to Ornan, Ornan looked and saw David, and went out of the threshingfloor, and bowed himself to David with his face to the ground.

22 Then David said to Ornan, Grant me the place of this threshingfloor, that I may build an altar therein unto the Lord: thou shalt grant it me for the full price: that the plague may be stayed from the people.

23 And Ornan said unto David, Take it to thee, and let my lord the king do that which is good in his eyes: lo, I give thee the oxen also for burnt offerings, and the threshing instruments for wood, and the wheat for the meat offering; I give it all.

24 And king David said to Ornan, Nay; but I will verily buy it for the full price: for I will not take that which is thine for the Lord, nor offer burnt offerings without cost.

25 So David gave to Ornan for the place six hundred shekels of gold by weight.

26 And David built there an altar unto the Lord, and offered burnt offerings and peace offerings, and called upon the Lord; and he answered him from heaven by fire upon the altar of burnt offering.

27 And the LORD commanded the angel; and he put up his sword again into the sheath thereof.

28 At that time when David saw that the LORD had answered him in the threshingfloor of Ornan the Jebusite, then he sacrificed there.

29 For the tabernacle of the LORD, which Moses made in the wilderness, and the altar of the burnt offering, were at that season in the high place at Gibeon.

30 But David could not go before it to enquire of God: for he was afraid because of the sword of the angel of the LORD.

Overview

As long as we are on this earth and battling our flesh, every one of us will have times when we sin. When we do, the Holy Spirit is faithful to convict us and to urge us to confess our sin and restore our relationship with God. At that moment of conviction, we choose between resisting the Holy Spirit in pride or responding with a heart of repentance. In this lesson, we will see such a time in David's life and how he displayed repentance from the heart.

Introduction

_____

_____

_____

ROMANS 3:23

23 For all have sinned, and come short of the glory of God;

Keep a tender heart.

HEBREWS 4:7

7 ...To day if ye will hear his voice, harden not your hearts. *become callous*

ACTS 7:51

51 Ye stiffnecked and uncircumcised in heart and ears, ye do always resist the Holy Ghost: as your fathers did, so do ye.

PSALM 51:1

1 Have mercy upon me, O God, according to thy lovingkindness: according unto the multitude of thy tender mercies blot out my transgressions.

I. The _Rebellion_ of David

A. A _Planted_ Thought

1 CHRONICLES 21:1

1 And Satan stood up against Israel, and provoked David to number Israel.

2 CORINTHIANS 10:5

5 Casting down imaginations, and every high thing that exalteth itself against the knowledge of God, and bringing into captivity every thought to the obedience of Christ;

JAMES 1:13–15

13 Let no man say when he is tempted, I am tempted of God: for God cannot be tempted with evil, neither tempteth he any man:
14 But every man is tempted, when he is drawn away of his own lust, and enticed.

15 *Then when lust hath conceived, it bringeth forth sin: and sin, when it is finished, bringeth forth death.*

B. A _Precise_ Count

1 CHRONICLES 21:2

2 *And David said to Joab and to the rulers of the people, Go, number Israel from Beer-sheba even to Dan; and bring the number of them to me, that I may know it.*

1 CHRONICLES 21:3

3 *And Joab answered, The LORD make his people an hundred times so many more as they be: but, my lord the king, are they not all my lord's servants? why then doth my lord require this thing? why will he be a cause of trespass to Israel?*

PROVERBS 27:6

6 *Faithful are the wounds of a friend; but the kisses of an enemy are deceitful.*

PROVERBS 1:30–31

30 *They would none of my counsel: they despised all my reproof.*
31 *Therefore shall they eat of the fruit of their own way, and be filled with their own devices.*

1 CHRONICLES 21:4

4 *Nevertheless the king's word prevailed against Joab...*

II. The _Repentance_ of David

1 CHRONICLES 21:7

7   And God was displeased with this thing; therefore he smote Israel.

A. He _acknowledged Repented of_ His Sin

1 CHRONICLES 21:8

8   And David said unto God, I have sinned greatly, because I have done this thing: but now, I beseech thee, do away the iniquity of thy servant; for I have done very foolishly.

2 SAMUEL 24:10

10   And David's heart smote him after that he had numbered the people. And David said unto the LORD, I have sinned greatly in that I have done: and now, I beseech thee, O LORD, take away the iniquity of thy servant; for I have done very foolishly.

PSALM 51:4

4   Against thee, thee only, have I sinned, and done this evil in thy sight: that thou mightest be justified when thou speakest, and be clear when thou judgest.

1 JOHN 1:9

9   If we confess our sins, he is faithful and just to forgive us our sins, and to cleanse us from all unrighteousness.

B. He _Accepted_ the Consequences

1 Chronicles 21:11–14

11 So Gad came to David, and said unto him, Thus saith the Lord, Choose thee

12 Either three years' famine; or three months to be destroyed before thy foes, while that the sword of thine enemies overtaketh thee; or else three days the sword of the Lord, even the pestilence, in the land, and the angel of the Lord destroying throughout all the coasts of Israel. Now therefore advise thyself what word I shall bring again to him that sent me.

13 And David said unto Gad, I am in a great strait: let me fall now into the hand of the Lord; for very great are his mercies: but let me not fall into the hand of man.

14 So the Lord sent pestilence upon Israel: and there fell of Israel seventy thousand men.

Hebrews 12:5–6, 11

5 And ye have forgotten the exhortation which speaketh unto you as unto children, My son, despise not thou the chastening of the Lord, nor faint when thou art rebuked of him:

6 For whom the Lord loveth he chasteneth, and scourgeth every son whom he receiveth.

11 Now no chastening for the present seemeth to be joyous, but grievous: nevertheless afterward it yieldeth the peaceable fruit of righteousness unto them which are exercised thereby.

Revelation 3:19

19 As many as I love, I rebuke and chasten: be zealous therefore, and repent.

C. He _Interceded_ for His People

1 CHRONICLES 21:16–17

16 And David lifted up his eyes, and saw the angel of the LORD stand between the earth and the heaven, having a drawn sword in his hand stretched out over Jerusalem. Then David and the elders of Israel, who were clothed in sackcloth, fell upon their faces.

17 And David said unto God, Is it not I that commanded the people to be numbered? even I it is that have sinned and done evil indeed; but as for these sheep, what have they done? let thine hand, I pray thee, O LORD my God, be on me, and on my father's house; but not on thy people, that they should be plagued.

III. The _Remembrance_ of David

1 CHRONICLES 21:18–21

18 Then the angel of the LORD commanded Gad to say to David, that David should go up, and set up an altar unto the LORD in the threshingfloor of Ornan the Jebusite.

19 And David went up at the saying of Gad, which he spake in the name of the LORD.

20 And Ornan turned back, and saw the angel; and his four sons with him hid themselves. Now Ornan was threshing wheat.

21 And as David came to Ornan, Ornan looked and saw David, and went out of the threshingfloor, and bowed himself to David with his face to the ground.

1 JOHN 1:7

7 ...the blood of Jesus Christ his Son cleanseth us from all sin.

2 CHRONICLES 3:1

1   Then Solomon began to build the house of the
LORD at Jerusalem in mount Moriah, where the LORD
appeared unto David his father, in the place that David
had prepared in the threshingfloor of Ornan the Jebusite.

A. David's Sacrifice Was *Costly*

1 CHRONICLES 21:22–23

22   Then David said to Ornan, Grant me the place of
this threshingfloor, that I may build an altar therein
unto the LORD: thou shalt grant it me for the full price:
that the plague may be stayed from the people.
23   And Ornan said unto David, Take it to thee, and
let my lord the king do that which is good in his eyes:
lo, I give thee the oxen also for burnt offerings, and the
threshing instruments for wood, and the wheat for the
meat offering; I give it all.

B. David's Sacrifice Was *Personal*

1 CHRONICLES 21:24

24   And king David said to Ornan, Nay; but I will
verily buy it for the full price: for I will not take that
which is thine for the LORD, nor offer burnt offerings
without cost.

1 CHRONICLES 21:25–26

25   So David gave to Ornan for the place six hundred
shekels of gold by weight.
26   And David built there an altar unto the LORD,
and offered burnt offerings and peace offerings, and

called upon the LORD; and he answered him from heaven by fire upon the altar of burnt offering.

2 CORINTHIANS 8:2–5

2   How that in a great trial of affliction the abundance of their joy and their deep poverty abounded unto the riches of their liberality.

3   For to their power, I bear record, yea, and beyond their power they were willing of themselves;

4   Praying us with much intreaty that we would receive the gift, and take upon us the fellowship of the ministering to the saints.

5   And this they did, not as we hoped, but first gave their own selves to the Lord, and unto us by the will of God.

1 CHRONICLES 21:27–28

27   And the LORD commanded the angel; and he put up his sword again into the sheath thereof.

28   At that time when David saw that the LORD had answered him in the threshingfloor of Ornan the Jebusite, then he sacrificed there.

Conclusion

1 CHRONICLES 21:26

26   ...and he answered him from heaven by fire upon the altar of burnt offering.

_____

_____

_____

Study Questions

1. Where do temptation and sin always begin?

2. What is the mark of a good friend? Do you have friends like this in your life? Are you willing to be that kind of friend for someone else?

3. We all sin, and God convicts all of us. But we don't all have the same response. What are the two ways that people respond to God's conviction?

4. What are the three evidences of genuine repentance we saw from David's life in this lesson?

5. What does 1 John 1:9 tell us God promises to do when we acknowledge (or confess) our sin to God?

6. Why does God allow consequences (chastening) of our sin even after we confess it to Him?

7. How do we see the sincerity and tenderness of David's heart in his sacrifice?

8. What is the result of living with a repentant, tender heart to the Lord?

Memory Verse

1 JOHN 1:9
9 *If we confess our sins, he is faithful and just to forgive us our sins, and to cleanse us from all unrighteousness.*

Humility

Text

Broke & Comfort
Contentment

PHILIPPIANS 2:1–8

1   *If there be therefore any consolation in Christ, if any comfort of love, if any fellowship of the Spirit, if any bowels and mercies,*

2   *Fulfil ye my joy, that ye be likeminded, having the same love, being of one accord, of one mind.*

3   *Let nothing be done through strife or vainglory; but in lowliness of mind let each esteem other better than themselves.*

4   *Look not every man on his own things, but every man also on the things of others.*

5   *Let this mind be in you, which was also in Christ Jesus:*

6   *Who, being in the form of God, thought it not robbery to be equal with God:*

7   *But made himself of no reputation, and took upon him the form of a servant, and was made in the likeness of men:*

8   *And being found in fashion as a man, he humbled himself, and became obedient unto death, even the death of the cross.*

Overview

We live in a world saturated with pride. Yet, nothing will destroy our spiritual foundation so effectively as undetected pride in our own lives.

God calls us to walk in humility. He instructs us to allow the mind of Christ—described in Philippians 2 as a mind of humility—to be in us. In this lesson, we will look at the characteristics of a person who seeks to walk in humility.

Introduction

Characteristic of person (handwritten)

ROMANS 8:29

29 For whom he did foreknow, he also did predestinate to be conformed to the image of his Son, that he might be the firstborn among many brethren.

PHILIPPIANS 2:5

Think like Him (handwritten)

5 Let this **mind** be in you, which was also in Christ Jesus:

PHILIPPIANS 2:6–8

6 Who, being in the form of God, thought it not robbery to be equal with God:

7 But made himself of no reputation, and took upon him the form of a servant, and was made in the likeness of men:

8 And being found in fashion as a man, he humbled himself, and became obedient unto death, even the death of the cross.

PROVERBS 18:12

12 Before destruction the heart of man is haughty, and before honour is humility.

PROVERBS 22:4

4 By humility and the fear of the LORD are riches, and honour, and life.

PROVERBS 11:2

2 When pride cometh, then cometh shame: but with the lowly is wisdom.

PROVERBS 16:18

18 *Pride goeth before destruction, and an haughty spirit before a fall.*

JAMES 4:10

10 *Humble yourselves in the sight of the Lord, and he shall lift you up.*

I. Seek a Walk of *Unity*

PHILIPPIANS 2:1–2

1 *If there be therefore any consolation in Christ, if any comfort of love, if any fellowship of the Spirit, if any bowels and mercies,*

2 *Fulfil ye my joy, that ye be likeminded, having the same love, being of one accord, of one mind.*

A. It Is Based on Our *fellowship* in Christ

PHILIPPIANS 2:1

encouragement

1 *If there be therefore any consolation in Christ, if* *calming / encouraging* *any comfort of love, if any fellowship of the Spirit, if* *communing* *any bowels and mercies,*

a gospel of love *emotions*

JOHN 15:26

26 *But when the Comforter is come, whom I will send unto you from the Father, even the Spirit of truth, which proceedeth from the Father, he shall testify of me:*

GALATIANS 5:22

22 *But the fruit of the Spirit is* **love,** *joy, peace, longsuffering, gentleness, goodness, faith,*

41

B. It Is Evidenced by the *Character* of Christ

PHILIPPIANS 2:2

2 *Fulfil ye my joy, that ye be likeminded, having the same love, being of one accord, of one mind.*

1 JOHN 4:11

11 *Beloved, if God so loved us, we ought also to love one another.*

EPHESIANS 4:3

3 *Endeavouring to keep the unity of the Spirit in the bond of peace.*

PHILIPPIANS 1:27

27 *Only let your conversation be as it becometh the gospel of Christ: that whether I come and see you, or else be absent, I may hear of your affairs, that ye stand fast in one spirit, with one mind striving together for the faith of the gospel;*

II. Separate from *Contention*

PHILIPPIANS 2:3

3 *Let nothing be done through strife or vainglory; but in lowliness of mind let each esteem other better than themselves.*

A. Refuse *Strife*

PHILIPPIANS 2:3

3 *Let nothing be done through strife...*

PROVERBS 26:20

20 Where no wood is, there the fire goeth out: so where there is no talebearer, the strife ceaseth.

PROVERBS 26:22

22 The words of a talebearer are as wounds, and they go down into the innermost parts of the belly.

JAMES 3:16

16 For where envying and strife is, there is confusion and every evil work.

EPHESIANS 4:29

29 Let no corrupt communication proceed out of your mouth, but that which is good to the use of edifying, that it may minister grace unto the hearers.

2 TIMOTHY 2:4

4 No man that warreth entangleth himself with the affairs of this life; that he may please him who hath chosen him to be a soldier.

B. Maintain _Lowliness_ of Mind

PHILIPPIANS 2:3

3 ...or vainglory; but in lowliness of mind...

GALATIANS 6:3

3 For if a man think himself to be something, when he is nothing, he deceiveth himself.

ROMANS 12:3

3 For I say, through the grace given unto me, to every man that is among you, not to think of himself more highly than he ought to think; but to think soberly,

according as God hath dealt to every man the measure of faith.

EPHESIANS 4:31–32

31 Let all bitterness, and wrath, and anger, and clamour, and evil speaking, be put away from you, with all malice:

32 And be ye kind one to another, tenderhearted, forgiving one another, even as God for Christ's sake hath forgiven you.

C. Esteem _____*others*_____ Better

PHILIPPIANS 2:3

3 …let each esteem other better than themselves.

1 PETER 5:5

5 …Yea, all of you be subject one to another, and be clothed with humility: for God resisteth the proud, and giveth grace to the humble.

III. Serve _____*Others*_____ in Need

PHILIPPIANS 2:4

4 Look not every man on his own things, but every man also on the things of others.

LUKE 22:27

27 For whether is greater, he that sitteth at meat, or he that serveth? is not he that sitteth at meat? but I am among you as he that serveth.

A. It Is an _Unselfish_ Look

PHILIPPIANS 2:4

4 Look not every man on his own things…

B. It Is an _Outward_ Look

PHILIPPIANS 2:4

4 …but every man also on the things of others.

JAMES 1:27

27 Pure religion and undefiled before God and the Father is this, To visit the fatherless and widows in their affliction, and to keep himself unspotted from the world.

GALATIANS 5:13

13 For, brethren, ye have been called unto liberty; only use not liberty for an occasion to the flesh, but by love serve one another.

Conclusion

PHILIPPIANS 2:5

5 Let this mind be in you, which was also in Christ Jesus:

_____

_____

_____

Study Questions

1. Why would a Christian want unity?

2. Who is our greatest example of humility?

3. How is unity achieved?

4. What are the three characteristics of a person seeking to walk in humility?

5. According to Philippians 2:3, how do we separate from contention?

6. Is there anyone with whom you struggle to get along? How can you practically apply Philippians 2:1–2 in your relationship with that person this week?

7. What was Jesus' response to the disciples as they bickered over who would be the greatest in Heaven?

8. Considering James 1:27, what are ways that you can have an outward look? Who can you serve who needs to be served, and how?

Memory Verses

PHILIPPIANS 2:1–2

1 *If there be therefore any consolation in Christ, if any comfort of love, if any fellowship of the Spirit, if any bowels and mercies,*

2 *Fulfil ye my joy, that ye be likeminded, having the same love, being of one accord, of one mind.*

A Good Conscience

Text

ACTS 24:1–16

1 And after five days Ananias the high priest descended with the elders, and with a certain orator named Tertullus, who informed the governor against Paul.

2 And when he was called forth, Tertullus began to accuse him, saying, Seeing that by thee we enjoy great quietness, and that very worthy deeds are done unto this nation by thy providence,

3 We accept it always, and in all places, most noble Felix, with all thankfulness.

4 Notwithstanding, that I be not further tedious unto thee, I pray thee that thou wouldest hear us of thy clemency a few words.

5 For we have found this man a pestilent fellow, and a mover of sedition among all the Jews throughout the world, and a ringleader of the sect of the Nazarenes:

6 Who also hath gone about to profane the temple: whom we took, and would have judged according to our law.

7 But the chief captain Lysias came upon us, and with great violence took him away out of our hands,

8 Commanding his accusers to come unto thee: by examining of whom thyself mayest take knowledge of all these things, whereof we accuse him.

9 And the Jews also assented, saying that these things were so.

10 Then Paul, after that the governor had beckoned unto him to speak, answered, Forasmuch as I know that thou hast been of many years a judge unto this nation, I do the more cheerfully answer for myself:

11 Because that thou mayest understand, that there are yet but twelve days since I went up to Jerusalem for to worship.

12 And they neither found me in the temple disputing with any man, neither raising up the people, neither in the synagogues, nor in the city:

13 Neither can they prove the things whereof they now accuse me.

14 But this I confess unto thee, that after the way which they call heresy, so worship I the God of my fathers, believing all things which are written in the law and in the prophets:

15 And have hope toward God, which they themselves also allow, that there shall be a resurrection of the dead, both of the just and unjust.

16 And herein do I exercise myself, to have always a conscience void to offence toward God, and toward men.

Overview

Building below the baseline requires living with a good conscience. Our conscience is so important! The Apostle Paul speaks of the state of our conscience in several passages. We are going to study God's Word to understand the role of our conscience and how to have a good conscience that is void of offense toward God and toward men.

Introduction

_____

_____

_____

ACTS 24:16

16 And herein do I exercise myself, to have always a conscience void of offence toward God, and toward men.

I. The Conscience _Defined_

HEBREWS 4:12

12 For the word of God is quick, and powerful, and sharper than any twoedged sword, piercing even to the dividing asunder of soul and spirit, and of the joints and marrow, and is a discerner of the thoughts and intents of the heart.

A. The _Good_ Conscience _Developed Consistently_

ACTS 23:1

1 And Paul, earnestly beholding the council, said, Men and brethren, I have lived in all good conscience before God until this day.

1 TIMOTHY 1:18–19

18 This charge I commit unto thee, son Timothy, according to the prophecies which went before on thee, that thou by them mightest war a good warfare;

19 Holding faith, and a good conscience; which some having put away concerning faith have made shipwreck:

2 TIMOTHY 1:3

3 I thank God, whom I serve from my forefathers with pure conscience, that without ceasing I have remembrance of thee in my prayers night and day;

TITUS 2:11–12

11 For the grace of God that bringeth salvation hath appeared to all men,

12 Teaching us that, denying ungodliness and worldly lusts, we should live soberly, righteously, and godly, in this present world;

2 CORINTHIANS 1:12

12 For our rejoicing is this, the testimony of our conscience, that in simplicity and godly sincerity, not with fleshly wisdom, but by the grace of God, we have had our conversation in the world, and more abundantly to you-ward.

B. The _Defiled_ Conscience

TITUS 1:15–16

15 Unto the pure all things are pure: but unto them that are defiled and unbelieving is nothing pure; but even their mind and conscience is defiled.

16 They profess that they know God; but in works they deny him, being abominable, and disobedient, and unto every good work reprobate.

C. The _Evil_ Conscience

HEBREWS 10:22–23

22 Let us draw near with a true heart in full assurance of faith, having our hearts sprinkled from an evil conscience, and our bodies washed with pure water.

23 Let us hold fast the profession of our faith without wavering; (for he is faithful that promised;)

2 PETER 2:7–8

7 And delivered just Lot, vexed with the filthy conversation of the wicked:

8 (For that righteous man dwelling among them, in seeing and hearing, vexed his righteous soul from day to day with their unlawful deeds;)

Scorched
Dry as a bone

D. The _Seared_ Conscience

1 TIMOTHY 4:1–2

1 Now the Spirit speaketh expressly, that in the latter times some shall depart from the faith, giving heed to seducing spirits, and doctrines of devils;

2 Speaking lies in hypocrisy; having their conscience seared with a hot iron;

II. A Good Conscience _Exercise_

ACTS 24:16   _Develop consistently_

16 And herein do I exercise myself, to have always a conscience void to offence toward God, and toward men.

53

A. Exercise Requires a <u>Goal</u>

1 CORINTHIANS 9:25

25 And every man that striveth for the mastery is temperate in all things. Now they do it to obtain a corruptible crown; but we an incorruptible.

1 THESSALONIANS 4:1

1 Furthermore then we beseech you, brethren, and exhort you by the Lord Jesus, that as ye have received of us how ye ought to walk and to please God, so ye would abound more and more.

2 TIMOTHY 2:4

4 No man that warreth entangleth himself with the affairs of this life; that he may please him who hath chosen him to be a soldier.

B. Exercise Requires <u>Discipline</u>

1 CORINTHIANS 9:27

27 But I keep under my body, and bring it into subjection: lest that by any means, when I have preached to others, I myself should be a castaway.

1 TIMOTHY 4:16

16 Take heed unto thyself, and unto the doctrine; continue in them: for in doing this thou shalt both save thyself, and them that hear thee.

PHILIPPIANS 2:12–13

12 Wherefore, my beloved,…work out your own salvation with fear and trembling.

13 For it is God which worketh in you both to will and to do of his good pleasure.

HEBREWS 12:1

1 Wherefore seeing we also are compassed about with so great a cloud of witnesses, let us lay aside every weight, and the sin which doth so easily beset us, and let us run with patience the race that is set before us,

EPHESIANS 5:18

18 And be not drunk with wine, wherein is excess; but be filled with the Spirit;

III. A Good Conscience _Displayed_

ACTS 24:16

16 And herein do I exercise myself, to have always a conscience void of offence **toward God, and toward men.**

A. Toward _God_

MATTHEW 5:8

8 Blessed are the pure in heart: for they shall see God.

1 SAMUEL 16:7

7 But the LORD said unto Samuel, Look not on his countenance, or on the height of his stature; because I have refused him: for the LORD seeth not as man seeth; for man looketh on the outward appearance, but the LORD looketh on the heart.

JAMES 4:8

8 *Draw nigh to God, and he will draw nigh to you. Cleanse your hands, ye sinners; and purify your hearts, ye double minded.*

B. Toward *Men*

MATTHEW 5:14–16

14 *Ye are the light of the world. A city that is set on an hill cannot be hid.*

15 *Neither do men light a candle, and put it under a bushel, but on a candlestick; and it giveth light unto all that are in the house.*

16 *Let your light so shine before men, that they may see your good works, and glorify your Father which is in heaven.*

2 CORINTHIANS 4:2

2 *But have renounced the hidden things of dishonesty, not walking in craftiness, nor handling the word of God deceitfully; but by manifestation of the truth commending ourselves to every man's conscience in the sight of God.*

2 CORINTHIANS 6:17

17 *Wherefore come out from among them, and be ye separate, saith the Lord, and touch not the unclean thing; and I will receive you.*

1 CORINTHIANS 8:9–13

9 *But take heed lest by any means this liberty of yours become a stumblingblock to them that are weak.*

10 For if any man see thee which hast knowledge sit at meat in the idol's temple, shall not the conscience of him which is weak be emboldened to eat those things which are offered to idols;

11 And through thy knowledge shall the weak brother perish, for whom Christ died?

12 But when ye sin so against the brethren, and wound their weak conscience, ye sin against Christ.

13 Wherefore, if meat make my brother to offend, I will eat no flesh while the world standeth, lest I make my brother to offend.

1 TIMOTHY 1:11

11 According to the glorious gospel of the blessed God, which was committed to my trust.

MATTHEW 28:19–20

19 Go ye therefore, and teach all nations, baptizing them in the name of the Father, and of the Son, and of the Holy Ghost:

20 Teaching them to observe all things whatsoever I have commanded you: and, lo, I am with you alway, even unto the end of the world. Amen.

Conclusion

1 PETER 3:15–16

15 But sanctify the Lord God in your hearts: and be ready always to give an answer to every man that asketh you a reason of the hope that is in you with meekness and fear:

16 Having a good conscience; that, whereas they speak evil of you, as of evildoers, they may be ashamed that falsely accuse your good conversation in Christ.

Study Questions

1. What are the four types of consciences we looked at in this lesson?

2. Having a good conscience isn't about being sinless. What is it?

3. What is a defiled conscience?

4. What is an evil conscience?

5. What is a seared conscience?

6. What is the goal of maintaining a good conscience?

7. What are the two disciplines of exercising a good conscience?

8. How can we maintain a good conscience toward men?

Memory Verses

1 PETER 3:15–16

15 But sanctify the Lord God in your hearts: and be ready always to give an answer to every man that asketh you a reason of the hope that is in you with meekness and fear:
16 Having a good conscience; that, whereas they speak evil of you, as of evildoers, they may be ashamed that falsely accuse your good conversation in Christ.

Dying to Self

Text

ROMANS 6:1–13

1   What shall we say then? Shall we continue in sin, that grace may abound?

2   God forbid. How shall we, that are dead to sin, live any longer therein?

3   Know ye not, that so many of us as were baptized into Jesus Christ were baptized into his death?

4   Therefore we are buried with him by baptism into death: that like as Christ was raised up from the dead by the glory of the Father, even so we also should walk in newness of life.

5   For if we have been planted together in the likeness of his death, we shall be also in the likeness of his resurrection:

6   Knowing this, that our old man is crucified with him, that the body of sin might be destroyed, that henceforth we should not serve sin.

7   For he that is dead is freed from sin.

8   Now if we be dead with Christ, we believe that we shall also live with him:

9   Knowing that Christ being raised from the dead dieth no more; death hath no more dominion over him.

10   For in that he died, he died unto sin once: but in that he liveth, he liveth unto God.

11   Likewise reckon ye also yourselves to be dead indeed unto sin, but alive unto God through Jesus Christ our Lord.

12 *Let not sin therefore reign in your mortal body, that ye should obey it in the lusts thereof.*

13 *Neither yield ye your members as instruments of unrighteousness unto sin: but yield yourselves unto God, as those that are alive from the dead, and your members as instruments of righteousness unto God.*

GALATIANS 2:20

20 *I am crucified with Christ: nevertheless I live; yet not I, but Christ liveth in me: and the life which I now live in the flesh I live by the faith of the Son of God, who loved me, and gave himself for me.*

Overview

God desires for each one of us to enjoy victorious Christian living. It is a vital element of building below the baseline. Yet, many struggle through their Christian life.

The equation for victorious Christian living is found in Romans 6 and Galatians 2:20. It is as we understand that our old nature is crucified with Christ and as we yield to the Holy Spirit that we are able to access this victory.

Introduction

_____

_____

_____

Romans 5—Justification	Romans 6—Sanctification
1. Christ died for us	1. We died with Christ
2. Substitution	2. Identification
3. Christ died for sins	3. Christ died unto sin
4. He paid sin's penalty	4. He broke sin's power
5. Righteousness imputed	5. Righteousness imparted

I. A Presumption to _Avoid_

ROMANS 6:1–2

1 _What shall we say then? Shall we continue in sin, that grace may abound?_

2 _God forbid. How shall we, that are dead to sin, live any longer therein?_

Using grace in salvation to continue in sin

A. A Problem of _Interpretation_

2 TIMOTHY 2:15

15 _Study to shew thyself approved unto God, a workman that needeth not to be ashamed, **rightly dividing the word of truth.**_

2 TIMOTHY 3:16–17

16 **_All scripture is given by inspiration of God,_** _and is profitable for doctrine, for reproof, for correction, for instruction in righteousness:_

17 *That the man of God may be perfect, thoroughly furnished unto all good works.*

B. A Problem of *Intention*

HEBREWS 4:12

12 *For the word of God is quick, and powerful, and sharper than any twoedged sword, piercing even to the dividing asunder of soul and spirit, and of the joints and marrow, **and is a discerner of the thoughts and intents of the heart.***

ROMANS 6:1–2

1 *What shall we say then? Shall we continue in sin, that grace may abound?*

2 *God forbid. How shall we, that are dead to sin, live any longer therein?*

TITUS 2:11–14

11 *For the grace of God that bringeth salvation hath appeared to all men,*

12 *Teaching us that, denying ungodliness and worldly lusts, we should live soberly, righteously, and godly, in this present world;*

13 *Looking for that blessed hope, and the glorious appearing of the great God and our Saviour Jesus Christ;*

14 *Who gave himself for us, that he might **redeem** us from all iniquity, and **purify** unto himself a peculiar people, zealous of good works.*

GALATIANS 5:13

13 For, brethren, ye have been called unto liberty; only use not liberty for an occasion to the flesh, but by love serve one another.

II. A Position to _Acknowledge_

ROMANS 6:3–5

3 Know ye not, that so many of us as were baptized into Jesus Christ were baptized into his death?

4 Therefore we are buried with him by baptism into death: that like as Christ was raised up from the dead by the glory of the Father, even so we also should walk in newness of life.

5 For if we have been planted together in the likeness of his death, we shall be also in the likeness of his resurrection:

A. _Crucified_ with Christ

GALATIANS 2:20

20 I am crucified with Christ: nevertheless I live; yet not I, but Christ liveth in me: and the life which I now live in the flesh I live by the faith of the Son of God, who loved me, and gave himself for me.

ROMANS 6:6

6 Knowing this, that our old man is crucified with him, that the body of sin might be destroyed, that henceforth we should not serve sin.

GALATIANS 2:20

20 *I am crucified with Christ...*

B. _Buried_ **with Christ**

ROMANS 6:3–4

3 *Know ye not, that so many of us as were baptized into Jesus Christ were baptized into his death?*

4 *Therefore we are buried with him by baptism into death...*

C. _Risen_ (Raised) **with Christ**   *alive in Christ* — *new nature*

ROMANS 6:4–9

4 *...that like as Christ was raised up from the dead by the glory of the Father, even so we also should walk in newness of life.*

5 *For if we have been planted together in the likeness of his death, we shall be also in the likeness of his resurrection:*

6 *Knowing this, that our old man is crucified with him, that the body of sin might be destroyed, that henceforth we should not serve sin.*

7 *For he that is dead is freed from sin.*

8 *Now if we be dead with Christ, we believe that we shall also live with him:*

9 *Knowing that Christ being raised from the dead dieth no more; death hath no more dominion over him.*

GALATIANS 2:20

20 *I am crucified with Christ: nevertheless I live; yet not I, but Christ liveth in me...*

2 Timothy 2:11

11   It is a faithful saying: For if we be dead with him, we shall also live with him:

Ephesians 4:22–24

22   That ye put off concerning the former conversation the old man, which is corrupt according to the deceitful lusts;

23   And be renewed in the spirit of your mind;

24   And that ye put on the new man, which after God is created in righteousness and true holiness.

John 10:10

10   The thief cometh not, but for to steal, and to kill, and to destroy: I am come that they might have life, and that they might have it more abundantly.

Colossians 3:3

3   For ye are dead, and your life is hid with Christ in God.

2 Corinthians 5:17

17   Therefore if any man be in Christ, he is a new creature: old things are passed away; behold, all things are become new.

III. A Process to   _Activate_

Galatians 2:20

20   I am crucified with Christ: nevertheless I live; yet not I, but Christ liveth in me: **and the life which I now live**

in the flesh I live by the faith of the Son of God, who
loved me, and gave himself for me.

EPHESIANS 5:8
8   *For ye were sometimes darkness, but now are ye light
in the Lord: walk as children of light:*

GALATIANS 5:24–25
24   *And they that are Christ's have crucified the flesh
with the affections and lusts.*
25   *If we live in the Spirit, let us also walk in the Spirit.*

A. *Reckon*

ROMANS 6:11
11   *Likewise reckon ye also yourselves to be dead
indeed unto sin, but alive unto God through Jesus
Christ our Lord.*

1 CORINTHIANS 15:31
31   *...I die daily.*

B. *Yield* (place oneself at
the disposal of)

ROMANS 6:13
13   *...but yield yourselves unto God, as those that are
alive from the dead, and your members as instruments
of righteousness unto God.*

ROMANS 6:12
12   *Let not sin therefore reign in your mortal body,
that ye should obey it in the lusts thereof.*

ROMANS 12:1–2

1   *I beseech you therefore, brethren, by the mercies of God, that* **ye present your bodies a living sacrifice,** *holy, acceptable unto God, which is your reasonable service.*

2   *And be not conformed to this world: but be ye transformed by the renewing of your mind, that ye may prove what is that good, and acceptable, and perfect, will of God.*

ROMANS 6:12–13

12   *Let not sin therefore reign in your mortal body, that ye should obey it in the lusts thereof.*

13   *Neither yield ye your members as instruments of unrighteousness unto sin: but yield yourselves unto God, as those that are alive from the dead, and your members as instruments of righteousness unto God.*

Conclusion

ROMANS 8:12–14

12   *Therefore, brethren, we are debtors, not to the flesh, to live after the flesh.*

13   *For if ye live after the flesh, ye shall die: but if ye through the Spirit do mortify the deeds of the body, ye shall live.*

14   *For as many as are led by the Spirit of God, they are the sons of God.*

_____

_____

_____

Study Questions

1. What is the presumption that needs to be avoided?

2. What is the correct way you can enjoy God's grace?

3. What are the three positions we are to acknowledge?

4. What is the process to activate dying to self?

5. According to Galatians 5:24–25, how do we not fulfill the lusts of the flesh?

6. What is the only way to have sustained longevity in the Christian life?

7. What is an area of sinful living that you have already seen God's grace give you the power to overcome?

8. What is an area that is a current source of temptation in which you need to reckon yourself dead to sin and yield to God for victory?

Memory Verse

GALATIANS 2:20

20 *I am crucified with Christ: nevertheless I live; yet not I, but Christ liveth in me: and the life which I now live in the flesh I live by the faith of the Son of God, who loved me, and gave himself for me.*

Filled with the Spirit

Text

EPHESIANS 5:15–21

15 *See then that ye walk circumspectly, not as fools, but as wise,*

16 *Redeeming the time, because the days are evil.*

17 *Wherefore be ye not unwise, but understanding what the will of the Lord is.*

18 *And be not drunk with wine, wherein is excess; but be filled with the Spirit;*

19 *Speaking to yourselves in psalms and hymns and spiritual songs, singing and making melody in your heart to the Lord;*

20 *Giving thanks always for all things unto God and the Father in the name of our Lord Jesus Christ;*

21 *Submitting yourselves one to another in the fear of God.*

Overview

Although every Christian possesses the Holy Spirit, not every Christian is *possessed* of the Holy Spirit. There is a huge difference between the two positions. God commands us multiple times in Scripture to be filled with His Spirit. But this is not something God forces upon us; rather, it is our choice to yield to the process. In this lesson, we will look at God's instructions for living a Spirit-filled life.

Introduction

_____

_____

_____

EPHESIANS 1:13–14

13 In whom ye also trusted, after that ye heard the word of truth, the gospel of your salvation: in whom also after that ye believed, ye were sealed with that holy Spirit of promise,
14 Which is the earnest of our inheritance until the redemption of the purchased possession, unto the praise of his glory.

I. The Spirit-Filled *Path*

GALATIANS 5:16

16 This I say then, Walk in the Spirit, and ye shall not fulfil the lust of the flesh.

A. A Path of *Caution*

EPHESIANS 5:15–16

15 See then that ye walk circumspectly, not as fools, but as wise,
16 Redeeming the time, because the days are evil.

COLOSSIANS 4:5

5 Walk in wisdom toward them that are without, redeeming the time.

1 PETER 5:8

8   Be sober, be vigilant; because your adversary the devil, as a roaring lion, walketh about, seeking whom he may devour:

B. A Path of *Consecration*

EPHESIANS 5:17

17   Wherefore be ye not unwise, but understanding what the will of the Lord is.

1 THESSALONIANS 4:3–4

*3   **For this is the will of God, even your sanctification,** that ye should abstain from fornication:*
4   That every one of you should know how to possess his vessel in sanctification and honour;

COLOSSIANS 3:16

16   Let the word of Christ dwell in you richly in all wisdom…

II. The Spirit-Filled _____

EPHESIANS 5:18

18   And be not drunk with wine, wherein is excess; but be filled with the Spirit;

A. A _____ Purpose

EPHESIANS 5:18

18   And be not drunk with wine…

PROVERBS 23:29–35

29 *Who hath woe? who hath sorrow? who hath contentions? who hath babbling? who hath wounds without cause? who hath redness of eyes?*

30 *They that tarry long at the wine; they that go to seek mixed wine.*

31 *Look not thou upon the wine when it is red, when it giveth his colour in the cup, when it moveth itself aright.*

32 *At the last it biteth like a serpent, and stingeth like an adder.*

33 *Thine eyes shall behold strange women, and thine heart shall utter perverse things.*

34 *Yea, thou shalt be as he that lieth down in the midst of the sea, or as he that lieth upon the top of a mast.*

35 *They have stricken me, shalt thou say, and I was not sick; they have beaten me, and I felt it not: when shall I awake? I will seek it yet again.*

B. A _____ Purpose

EPHESIANS 5:18

18 *...but be filled with the Spirit;*

ROMANS 6:13

13 *Neither yield ye your members as instruments of unrighteousness unto sin: but yield yourselves unto God, as those that are alive from the dead, and your members as instruments of righteousness unto God.*

2 CORINTHIANS 3:17

17 ...and where the Spirit of the Lord is, there is liberty.

III. The Spirit-Filled _____

EPHESIANS 5:19–21

19   Speaking to yourselves in psalms and hymns and spiritual songs, singing and making melody in your heart to the Lord;

20   Giving thanks always for all things unto God and the Father in the name of our Lord Jesus Christ;

21   Submitting yourselves one to another in the fear of God.

GALATIANS 5:22–25

22   But the fruit of the Spirit is love, joy, peace, longsuffering, gentleness, goodness, faith,

23   Meekness, temperance: against such there is no law.

24   And they that are Christ's have crucified the flesh with the affections and lusts.

25   If we live in the Spirit, let us also walk in the Spirit.

A. It Is a Product of _____

EPHESIANS 5:19

19   Speaking to yourselves in psalms and hymns and spiritual songs, singing and making melody in your heart to the Lord;

ACTS 16:25

25 And at midnight Paul and Silas prayed, and sang praises unto God: and the prisoners heard them.

COLOSSIANS 3:16

16 Let the word of Christ dwell in you richly in all wisdom; teaching and admonishing one another in psalms and hymns and spiritual songs, singing with grace in your hearts to the Lord.

PSALM 40:1–3

1 I waited patiently for the LORD; and he inclined unto me, and heard my cry.

2 He brought me up also out of an horrible pit, out of the miry clay, and set my feet upon a rock, and established my goings.

3 **And he hath put a new song in my mouth, even praise unto our God:** many shall see it, and fear, and shall trust in the LORD.

B. It Is a Product of _____

EPHESIANS 5:20

20 Giving thanks always for all things unto God and the Father in the name of our Lord Jesus Christ;

1 THESSALONIANS 5:18

18 In every thing give thanks: for this is the will of God in Christ Jesus concerning you.

C. It Is a Product of _____

EPHESIANS 5:21

21 *Submitting yourselves one to another in the fear of God.*

MARK 10:45

45 *For even the Son of man came not to be ministered unto, but to minister, and to give his life a ransom for many.*

Conclusion

_____

_____

_____

Study Questions

1. What is the difference in our lives related to the Holy Spirit between what happens at salvation and what we've discussed in this lesson?

2. What is the Spirit-filled path?

3. What does it mean to "walk circumspectly," and why is it so important?

4. What is the contrast Ephesians 5:18 gives to being filled with the Spirit? What does that tell us about what it means to be filled with the Spirit?

5. What ought to be the desire of every Christian?

6. We see in our text that the product of a Spirit-filled life is joy, gratitude, and cooperation. Do you see these in your life? Would others who know you well say they see them?

7. In what areas do you *not* see the product of the Spirit's filling in your life? What does that tell you about where and how you need to yield to the Holy Spirit?

8. What Christian do you know who seems to always radiate the joy, gratitude, and cooperation with others of the Spirit-filled life? How can you learn through their example?

Memory Verse

GALATIANS 5:16

16 *This I say then, Walk in the Spirit, and ye shall not fulfil the lust of the flesh.*

Spiritual Discipline

Text

1 CORINTHIANS 9:24–27

24 *Know ye not that they which run in a race run all, but one receiveth the prize? So run, that ye may obtain.*

25 *And every man that striveth for the mastery is temperate in all things. Now they do it to obtain a corruptible crown; but we an incorruptible.*

26 *I therefore so run, not as uncertainly; so fight I, not as one that beateth the air:*

27 *But I keep under my body, and bring it into subjection: lest that by any means, when I have preached to others, I myself should be a castaway.*

Overview

It may sound counterintuitive, but spiritual disciplines are not for the purpose of making us more spiritual. Nor are they to be a heavy imposition of religious rules or traditions. A Christian who is passionate to live a life pleasing to his Creator willingly places himself under complete submission to the Holy Spirit of God just as an athlete places himself under the training of a coach. In fact, this is the parallel God uses in Scripture to teach us the importance of building discipline below the baseline.

Introduction

_____

_____

_____

I. The _____ of Discipline

1 CORINTHIANS 9:24

24 *Know ye not that they which run in a race run all,
but one receiveth the prize? So run, that ye may obtain.*

A. To Run the _____

1 CORINTHIANS 9:24

24 *Know ye not that they which run in a race run all,
but one receiveth the prize?...*

HEBREWS 12:1

1 *Wherefore seeing we also are compassed about
with so great a cloud of witnesses, let us lay aside every
weight, and the sin which doth so easily beset us, and
let us run with patience the race that is set before us,*

PHILIPPIANS 3:7–8

7 *But what things were gain to me, those I counted
loss for Christ.*
8 *Yea doubtless, and I count all things but loss for
the excellency of the knowledge of Christ Jesus my
Lord: for whom I have suffered the loss of all things,
and do count them but dung, that I may win Christ,*

B. To Obtain the _____

1 CORINTHIANS 9:24

24 ...So run, that ye may obtain.

PHILIPPIANS 3:8–10, 13–14

8 Yea doubtless, and I count all things but loss for the excellency of the knowledge of Christ Jesus my Lord: for whom I have suffered the loss of all things, and do count them but dung, **that I may win Christ,**

9 **And be found in him,** not having mine own righteousness, which is of the law, but that which is through the faith of Christ, the righteousness which is of God by faith:

10 **That I may know him,** and the power of his resurrection, and the fellowship of his sufferings, being made conformable unto his death;

13 Brethren, I count not myself to have apprehended: but this one thing I do, forgetting those things which are behind, and reaching forth unto those things which are before,

14 I press toward the mark for the prize of the high calling of God in Christ Jesus.

ROMANS 8:29

29 For whom he did foreknow, he also did predestinate to be conformed to the image of his Son, that he might be the firstborn among many brethren.

II. The _____ of Discipline

1 CORINTHIANS 9:25–27

25 And every man that striveth for the mastery is temperate in all things. Now they do it to obtain a corruptible crown; but we an incorruptible.

26 I therefore so run, not as uncertainly; so fight I, not as one that beateth the air:

27 But I keep under my body, and bring it into subjection: lest that by any means, when I have preached to others, I myself should be a castaway.

1 PETER 5:8–9

8 Be sober, be vigilant; because your adversary the devil, as a roaring lion, walketh about, seeking whom he may devour:

9 Whom resist stedfast in the faith, knowing that the same afflictions are accomplished in your brethren that are in the world.

A. _____ in All Things

1 CORINTHIANS 9:25

25 And every man that striveth for the mastery is temperate in all things. Now they do it to obtain a corruptible crown; but we an incorruptible.

ROMANS 14:21

21 It is good neither to eat flesh, nor to drink wine, nor any thing whereby thy brother stumbleth, or is offended, or is made weak.

B. _____ **in All Things**

1 Corinthians 9:26

26 *I therefore so run, not as uncertainly; so fight I, not as one that beateth the air:*

1 Corinthians 9:19–22

19 *For though I be free from all men, yet have I made myself servant unto all, that I might gain the more.*
20 *And unto the Jews I became as a Jew, that I might gain the Jews; to them that are under the law, as under the law, that I might gain them that are under the law;*
21 *To them that are without law, as without law, (being not without law to God, but under the law to Christ,) that I might gain them that are without law.*
22 *To the weak became I as weak, that I might gain the weak:* **I am made all things to all men, that I might by all means save some.**

C. _____ **in All Things**

1 Corinthians 9:27

27 *But I keep under my body, and bring it into subjection: lest that by any means, when I have preached to others, I myself should be a castaway.*

Ephesians 5:18

18 *And be not drunk with wine, wherein is excess; but be filled with the Spirit;*

III. The _____ of Discipline

A. The _____

ROMANS 14:10–12

10 ...for we shall all stand before **the judgment seat of Christ.**

11 For it is written, As I live, saith the Lord, every knee shall bow to me, and every tongue shall confess to God.

12 So then every one of us shall give account of himself to God.

1 CORINTHIANS 3:12–15

12 Now if any man build upon this foundation gold, silver, precious stones, wood, hay, stubble;

13 **Every man's work shall be made manifest:** for the day shall declare it, because it shall be revealed by fire; and the fire shall try every man's work of what sort it is.

14 If any man's work abide which he hath built thereupon, **he shall receive a reward.**

15 If any man's work shall be burned, **he shall suffer loss:** but he himself shall be saved; yet so as by fire.

ECCLESIASTES 12:14

14 For God shall bring every work into judgment, with every secret thing, whether it be good, or whether it be evil.

LUKE 8:17

17 For nothing is secret, that shall not be made manifest; neither any thing hid, that shall not be known and come abroad.

B. The _____

2 Corinthians 5:10

10 For we must all appear before the judgment seat of Christ; that every one may receive the things done in his body, according to that he hath done, whether it be good or bad.

Matthew 25:23

23 His lord said unto him, Well done, good and faithful servant; thou hast been faithful over a few things, I will make thee ruler over many things: enter thou into the joy of thy lord.

Conclusion

1 Corinthians 9:25

25 And every man that striveth for the mastery is temperate in all things. Now they do it to obtain a corruptible crown; but we an incorruptible.

2 Timothy 4:6–8

6 For I am now ready to be offered, and the time of my departure is at hand.

7 I have fought a good fight, I have finished my course, I have kept the faith:

8 Henceforth there is laid up for me a crown of righteousness, which the Lord, the righteous judge, shall give me at that day: and not to me only, but unto all them also that love his appearing.

_____

_____

_____

Study Questions

1. Why do we need discipline in the Christian life?

2. What is the goal of the Christian life?

3. What does it mean to "strive for the mastery"?

4. What are some adversaries you face that challenge you in your race?

5. What does "temperate in all things" mean? What is one area in which you want to exercise more temperance?

6.   What is the prize of discipline?

7.   Are you living in daily awareness that you will one day stand before Christ?

8.   When you consider the judgment seat of Christ, what disciplines do you want to develop in your life today?

Memory Verse

1 CORINTHIANS 9:24

24 *Know ye not that they which run in a race run all, but one receiveth the prize? So run, that ye may obtain.*

Forgiveness

Text

EPHESIANS 4:26–32

26 Be ye angry, and sin not: let not the sun go down upon your wrath:

27 Neither give place to the devil.

28 Let him that stole steal no more: but rather let him labour, working with his hands the thing which is good, that he may have to give to him that needeth.

29 Let no corrupt communication proceed out of your mouth, but that which is good to the use of edifying, that it may minister grace unto the hearers.

30 And grieve not the holy Spirit of God, whereby ye are sealed unto the day of redemption.

31 Let all bitterness, and wrath, and anger, and clamour, and evil speaking, be put away from you, with all malice:

32 And be ye kind one to another, tenderhearted, forgiving one another, even as God for Christ's sake hath forgiven you.

Overview

God has bestowed His forgiveness upon us, even though it is completely undeserved. Yet within our relationships, we often struggle to forgive others. Unforgiveness cripples us, making us ineffective in our service for the Lord.

In this lesson, we will look at how God wants us to handle hurts, and we'll see the grace He offers us to forgive others.

Introduction

_____

_____

_____

I. Reject Satan's _____

A. To _____ in Anger

EPHESIANS 4:26
26 Be ye angry, and sin not:...

JAMES 1:20
20 For the wrath of man worketh not the righteousness of God.

MARK 3:5
5 And when he had looked round about on them with anger, being grieved for the hardness of their hearts, he saith unto the man, Stretch forth thine hand. And he stretched it out: and his hand was restored whole as the other.

ISAIAH 53:7
7 He was oppressed, and he was afflicted, yet he opened not his mouth: he is brought as a lamb to the slaughter, and as a sheep before her shearers is dumb, so he openeth not his mouth.

B. To _____ in Anger

EPHESIANS 4:26
26 ...let not the sun go down upon your wrath:

HEBREWS 12:15

15 *Looking diligently lest any man fail of the grace of God; lest any root of bitterness springing up trouble you, and thereby many be defiled;*

ROMANS 13:14

14 *But put ye on the Lord Jesus Christ, and make not provision for the flesh, to fulfil the lusts thereof.*

2 CORINTHIANS 2:10–11

10 *To whom ye forgive any thing, I forgive also: for if I forgave any thing, to whom I forgave it, for your sakes forgave I it in the person of Christ;*
11 *Lest Satan should get an advantage of us: for we are not ignorant of his devices.*

II. Reflect Biblical _____

A. In Our _____

EPHESIANS 4:28

28 *Let him that stole steal no more: but rather let him labour, working with his hands the thing which is good, that he may have to give to him that needeth.*

B. In Our _____

EPHESIANS 4:29

29 *Let no corrupt communication proceed out of your mouth, but that which is good to the use of edifying, that it may minister grace unto the hearers.*

JAMES 3:10–11

10 Out of the same mouth proceedeth blessing and cursing. My brethren, these things ought not so to be. 11 Doth a fountain send forth at the same place sweet water and bitter?

LUKE 4:22

22 And all bare him witness, and wondered at the gracious words which proceeded out of his mouth. And they said, Is not this Joseph's son?

JOHN 7:46

46 The officers answered, Never man spake like this man.

III. Refuse to _____ the Holy Spirit

EPHESIANS 4:30

30 And grieve not the holy Spirit of God, whereby ye are sealed unto the day of redemption.

A. _____ Grieves God

EPHESIANS 4:31

31 Let all bitterness, and wrath, and anger…be put away from you…

B. _____ Grieves God

EPHESIANS 4:31

31 Let all…clamour, and evil speaking, be put away from you, with all malice:

IV. Reflect the Saviour's _____

A. We Serve a _____ Saviour

EPHESIANS 4:32

32 And be ye kind one to another, tenderhearted…

B. We Serve a _____ Saviour

EPHESIANS 4:32

32 …forgiving one another, even as God for Christ's sake hath forgiven you.

LUKE 23:34

34 Then said Jesus, Father, forgive them; for they know not what they do. And they parted his raiment, and cast lots.

ROMANS 12:21

21 Be not overcome of evil, but overcome evil with good.

Conclusion

_____

_____

_____

Study Questions

1. What are some examples of how we see unforgiveness permeated throughout our culture?

2. How has God prepared a way for us to be free from the damage of unforgiveness and bitterness?

3. What are some of the tell-tale signs of an unforgiving spirit?

4. When wrongfully angered, we often will do things we never thought possible. Why is this?

5. In what two ways can we respond in biblical grace?

6. How do we cause sorrow and heaviness to the Holy Spirit?

7. Is there someone who often tends to make you feel angry? How can you show grace to them this week?

8. Is there someone whom you need to forgive? How does forgiving someone else set us free?

Memory Verse

EPHESIANS 4:32

32 *And be ye kind one to another, tenderhearted, forgiving one another, even as God for Christ's sake hath forgiven you.*

Contentment

Text

HEBREWS 13:5–6

5 Let your conversation be without covetousness; and be content with such things as ye have: for he hath said, I will never leave thee, nor forsake thee.

6 So that we may boldly say, The Lord is my helper, and I will not fear what man shall do unto me.

Overview

Learning to be content does not come naturally to anyone, nor is contentment promoted in our world. But a solid foundation below the baseline demands the structure of contentment.

Contentment is only found when we look to God for our sufficiency. It is then that we recognize that He is all we need. In this lesson, we will learn why we can be content and how we can develop contentment in our lives.

Introduction

_____

_____

_____

MATTHEW 7:24–27

*24 Therefore whosoever heareth these sayings of mine, and doeth them, I will liken him unto **a wise man, which built his house upon a rock**:*

25 And the rain descended, and the floods came, and the winds blew, and beat upon that house; and it fell not: for it was founded upon a rock.

*26 And every one that heareth these sayings of mine, and doeth them not, shall be likened unto **a foolish man, which built his house upon the sand**:*

27 And the rain descended, and the floods came, and the winds blew, and beat upon that house; and it fell: and great was the fall of it.

I. Build Contentment by Rejecting

_____

A. In Our _____

HEBREWS 13:5

5 Let your conversation be without covetousness…

EXODUS 20:17

17 Thou shalt not covet thy neighbour's house, thou shalt not covet thy neighbour's wife, nor his manservant, nor his maidservant, nor his ox, nor his ass, nor any thing that is thy neighbour's.

1 TIMOTHY 6:17

*17 Charge them that are rich in this world, that they be not highminded, **nor trust in uncertain riches, but in the living God,** who giveth us richly all things to enjoy;*

PROVERBS 23:4–5

4 Labour not to be rich: cease from thine own wisdom.

5 Wilt thou set thine eyes upon that which is not? for riches certainly make themselves wings; they fly away as an eagle toward heaven.

B. In Our _____

1 TIMOTHY 6:9–10

9 But they that will be rich fall into temptation and a snare, and into many foolish and hurtful lusts, which drown men in destruction and perdition.

10 For the love of money is the root of all evil: which while some coveted after, they have erred from the faith, and pierced themselves through with many sorrows.

LUKE 12:15

15 And he said unto them, Take heed, and beware of covetousness: for a man's life consisteth not in the abundance of the things which he possesseth.

II. Build Contentment By Remaining

HEBREWS 13:5

5   ...and be content with such things as ye have...

PHILIPPIANS 4:11

11   Not that I speak in respect of want: for I have learned, in whatsoever state I am, therewith to be content.

A. Because God Has Provided in the _____

PSALM 37:25

25   I have been young, and now am old; yet have I not seen the righteous forsaken, nor his seed begging bread.

1 KINGS 17:16

16   And the barrel of meal wasted not, neither did the cruse of oil fail, according to the word of the LORD, which he spake by Elijah.

B. Because God Will Provide for Our _____

HEBREWS 13:5

5   ...for he hath said, I will never leave thee, nor forsake thee.

MATTHEW 6:30–33

30   Wherefore, if God so clothe the grass of the field, which to day is, and to morrow is cast into the oven, shall he not much more clothe you, O ye of little faith?

31 Therefore take no thought, saying, What shall we eat? or, What shall we drink? or, Wherewithal shall we be clothed?

32 (For after all these things do the Gentiles seek:) for your heavenly Father knoweth that ye have need of all these things.

33 But seek ye first the kingdom of God, and his righteousness; and all these things shall be added unto you.

1 KINGS 8:56

56 Blessed be the LORD, that hath given rest unto his people Israel, according to all that he promised: there hath not failed one word of all his good promise, which he promised by the hand of Moses his servant.

III. Build Contentment By Renewing

_____

1 JOHN 4:4

4 Ye are of God, little children, and have overcome them: because greater is he that is in you, than he that is in the world.

A. By Remembering His _____

HEBREWS 13:5–6

5 ...for he hath said, I will never leave thee, nor forsake thee.

6 So that we may boldly say, The Lord is my helper...

TITUS 1:2

2   In hope of eternal life, which God, that cannot lie, promised before the world began;

DANIEL 3:25

25   He answered and said, Lo, I see four men loose, walking in the midst of the fire, and they have no hurt; and the form of the fourth is like the Son of God.

JOSHUA 1:9

9   Have not I commanded thee? Be strong and of a good courage; be not afraid, neither be thou dismayed: for the LORD thy God is with thee whithersoever thou goest.

B. By Remembering His _____

HEBREWS 13:6

6   ...and I will not fear what man shall do unto me.

PSALM 61:2–3

2   From the end of the earth will I cry unto thee, when my heart is overwhelmed: lead me to the rock that is higher than I.

3   For thou hast been a shelter for me, and a strong tower from the enemy.

ROMANS 8:26

26   Likewise the Spirit also helpeth our infirmities: for we know not what we should pray for as we ought: but the Spirit itself maketh intercession for us with groanings which cannot be uttered.

JAMES 1:17

17   Every good gift and every perfect gift is from above, and cometh down from the Father of lights, with whom is no variableness, neither shadow of turning.

ROMANS 8:31–32

31   What shall we then say to these things? If God be for us, who can be against us?

32   He that spared not his own Son, but delivered him up for us all, **how shall he not with him also freely give us all things?**

PSALM 37:1–3

1   Fret not thyself because of evildoers, neither be thou envious against the workers of iniquity.

2   For they shall soon be cut down like the grass, and wither as the green herb.

3   Trust in the LORD, and do good; so shalt thou dwell in the land, and verily thou shalt be fed.

Conclusion

_____

_____

_____

Study Questions

1. Discontentment is often seen in what we complain about. Think back over the past twenty-four hours of your life. What have you complained about? What have you praised God for?

2. What are the three ways God gives us in Hebrews 13:5–6 to build contentment in our lives?

3. The word *conversation* in Hebrews 13:5 means "your manner of life." How can contentment or discontentment be seen in our manner of life?

4. Discuss examples of modern day marketing that promote discontentment. What are things you deal with daily that promote the message of discontentment?

5. Where does contentment begin?

6. What are the two characteristics of God that ought to give us confidence in His sufficiency?

7. What promises of God do you need to remember this week?

8. Looking back over this *Build below the Baseline* series, which lessons have made the greatest difference in your life? What are three things you desire to purposefully implement as you move forward building below the baseline in your life?

Memory Verses

HEBREWS 13:5–6

5 *Let your conversation be without covetousness; and be content with such things as ye have: for he hath said, I will never leave thee, nor forsake thee.*

6 *So that we may boldly say, The Lord is my helper, and I will not fear what man shall do unto me.*

Striving Together
P u b l i c a t i o n s

For additional Christian
growth resources visit
strivingtogether.com